PERBACKS

THIS BLOOMSBURY

BELONG

*For children everywhere, whose voices go unheard.*

First published in Great Britain in 1998 by Bloomsbury Publishing Plc
38 Soho Square, London, W1V 5DF
This paperback edition first published 1999

Illustrations copyright © Debi Gliori 1998
The moral right of the illustrator has been asserted

A CIP catalogue record of this book is available from the British Library
ISBN 0 7475 4119 1 paperback
ISBN 0 7475 3554 X hardback

Designed by Dawn Apperley
Printed and bound by Proost, Belgium

1 3 5 7 9 10 8 6 4 2

# Give Him my Heart

## Debi Gliori

Based on a Poem by Christina Rossetti

BLOOMSBURY
CHILDREN'S
BOOKS

In the bleak
midwinter

Frosty wind made moan

Earth stood hard
as iron

# Water like a stone

Snow had fallen, snow on snow

Snow on snow

In the bleak midwinter
long, long ago

# What can I give Him poor as I am

If I were a
shepherd
I would bring
a lamb

If I were a wise man
I would do my part

# What I can I give Him

to Grandpa
with love

Give Him my heart

Acclaim for this book

'Any grandparent could get seriously misty-eyed over *Give Him My Heart*. The words are Christina Rossetti's 'In the Bleak Midwinter' and Debi Gliori's sweetly solemn pictures juxtapose a biblical interpretation with the story of a little [contemporary] girl making a Christmas gift to her grandad.'
*The Times*

'A gentle and sensitively illustrated reminder that Christmas is for giving, but not necessarily gifts of the material kind.'
M *Magazine*

FLC

# Asthma

For Jackie and Katy  F. C.    8/00

616

Text copyright © 1982, 1999 Althea Braithwaite
Illustrations copyright © 1999 Frances Cony

This edition first published 1999 by Happy Cat Books,
Bradfield, Essex CO11 2UT

A CIP catalogue record for this book is available from
the British Library

ISBN 1 899248 38 2 Paperback
ISBN 1 899248 33 1 Hardback

Printed in Hong Kong by Wing King Tong Co. Ltd